WORKBOC

THE OBESITY CODE

UNLOCKING

THE SECRETS OF

WEIGHT LOSS

By

DR. JASON FUNG

ORANGE Books

ISBN: 978-1-950284-29-0

Disclaimer: Terms of Use: Product names, logos, brands, and other trademarks featured or referred to within this publication are the property of their respective trademark holders and are not affiliated with this publication. The information in this book is meant for educational and entertainment purposes only and the publisher and author make no representations or warranties with respect to the accuracy or completeness of these contents and disclaim all warranties such as warranties of fitness for a particular purpose. This is an unofficial summary and analytical review meant for educational and entertainment purposes only and has not been authorized, approved, licensed, or endorsed by the original book's author or publisher and any of their licensees or affiliates.

Table of Contents

HOW TO USE THE WORKBOOK

In the book ***"The Obesity Code" by Dr. Jason Fung***, Dr. Fung led us to understand that everything we've been made to believe about how to lose weight is wrong. He went forward to state that weight gain and obesity are driven by hormones—in everyone—and only by understanding the effects of insulin and insulin resistance can we achieve lasting weight loss.

The goal of this Workbook is to help readers read, understand and practically begin to apply the major lessons from this great book "The Obesity code" by Dr Fung. So, as to be able to successfully loss weight and keep the fats away for good.

This workbook will help readers to start thinking logically and also help them in making preferable choices in life. It will also help open the reader up to a world of bliss, and expose him to areas hitherto untouched in the original book. But for this to be possible, it's advised that the reader diligently commits to answering the questions herein, so as to enjoy maximum satisfaction.

The lessons in this workbook are made easy and straightforward for readers to understand correctly; the **action steps** will enable the reader to learn the teachings of the original book. **The checklist** helps the readers to put themselves on check to become a better version of themselves. By providing answers to the questions in this workbook, the reader's expectation for getting this workbook must have been met

Remember, this is a weight loss book. Have fun, be patient with yourself, while you enjoy the journey using this workbook.

INTRODUCTION

The obesity code: unlocking the secrets of weight loss by Dr. Jason Fung is a good read! It seeks to correct all that you have believed about how to lose weight. Weight gain and obesity are driven by hormones, in everyone, and only by understanding the effects of insulin and insulin resistance can we achieve lasting weight loss.

This workbook is entirely different from the norm, as it takes you through a well- crafted, purposeful journey o transformation. You will be enlightened, as it helps you understand your body, weight, obesity and how to deal with all these, perfectly.

Be glued to this, and you'll learn, grow and achieve that body weight you dreamt of.

Enjoy!

PART 1: THE EPIDEMIC

CHAPTER 1: HOW OBESITY BECAME AN EPIDEMIC

For a long time now, a question has plagued my heart. Here it is: why are there fat doctors? Doctors are particularly seen as authorities with regards to subjects that surround the human physiology, and are expected to know the in and outs of the body system and its workings, obesity inclusive. In addition, lots of doctors are pretty disciplined and hardworking, and should know exactly what it takes to avoid being fat. Yet, there are still fat doctors. What then could the matter be?

In many cases, the popular prescription against being fat is to eat less and move more, which to a large extent makes perfect sense. Yet, this philosophy has failed time and again. While one could easily blame non-medical personnel for failing to follow this piece of advice, it wouldn't be logical to conclude that a doctor who had the tenacity to put up with long hours of medical study and all that came with it would find it impossible to follow their own advice. This brings us to just one conclusion: this advice is wrong. It is important therefore that we examine what obesity is, in itself.

The most important question that surrounds any disease is the cause. What causes it? Most people do not consider this question, as many already think the answer isn't far-fetched. I mean, we all assume that it is a calorie issue, and so, when we take in more calories than we burn, we gain weight. Eating too much and failing to exercise, or doing too little exercise also causes weight gain. All of these seemingly true statements are so convincing that we have never taken a step back to examine how true they really are.

Can I burst your bubble? You see, while excess calories might be a cause of weight gain, it is not the root cause. There are two types of causes: proximate and ultimate. In basic terms, proximate cause refers to an immediate cause, why the ultimate cause is that which birthed the series of events. In this case, obesity isn't caused mainly by consuming more calories than you expend. As a matter of fact, if we go by the previous argument, it would imply that obesity is borne from personal choice, since you would choose to eat chips instead of veggies, and so on. And if we go on with this argument, obesity goes from being a disease that needs to be examined and researched to becoming a failure on the part of the individual, a defect on the individual's character. Slowly and subtly, we imply that obese people brought the disease upon themselves, discriminating and detesting them. However, this idea of obesity is wrong.

History has it that man has not always been obsessed with calories. Even in our age long traditional societies, hardly did people become obese, the abundance of food notwithstanding. The advent of civilization however heralded the birth of obesity. Soon after, obesity was narrowed down to being caused by the refined carbohydrates of sugar and starches. It would soon be rediscovered that the refined carbohydrates did have largely fattening properties, resulting in the acceptance of diets low in refined carbohydrates as the major treatment for obesity. In the 1900s, calorie counting was introduced into the medical space. And coupled with the attendant deaths that took its toll on Americans as a result of heart related issues and diseases, dietary fat was blamed as the architect of all these. Quickly, physicians began to recommend diets that were low in fat. And the reduction of fats meant an increase in carbohydrates. What obtained in many developed countries of the world were highly refined carbohydrates. There was an imbalance. Carbohydrates couldn't both be good (low in fat) and bad (fattening) at the same time. Hence, to resolve the already brewing confusion, nutrition experts decided that carbohydrates were no longer fattening, but instead, calories were fattening. And without further investigation, the general assumption became that excess calories caused an increase in weight, and not some specific food. So, fat became the fattening object. However, not everyone agreed with this school of thought. Years later, British nutritionist would discover that no relationship existed between dietary fat and heart diseases, and instead, obesity and heart diseases were mainly caused by sugar.

LESSONS AND TAKEAWAYS

- Eat less, move more is a theory that will never work. it is simply wrong. It's been tested, and cannot be trusted to provide lasting results.
- Excess calories are not the ultimate cause of weight gain.
- Obesity is a hormonal disorder.
- There is no relationship between dietary fat and heart disease.

QUESTIONS

1. What is your weight story; are you overweight or underweight?

____

____

____

____

____

____

2. For how long have you been trying to shed or gain some pounds?

____

____

____

3. How has the journey been so far? Explain in details below.

____

____

____

____

____

____

____

4. What challenges did you encounter in your weight loss/ weight gain journey?

____

____

____

____

____

____

____

5. Were you able to achieve your desired weight size? If yes, explain how. If no, suggest reasons why.

____

____

____

____

6. Do you think your weight loss/ weight gain methods are effective? Provide reasons for your answer.

____

____

____

____

____

____

____

ACTION STEPS

- Understand that you do not have a character defect, neither is obesity your choice. Your hormones are responsible for your weight. Always have this at the back of your mind.
- Endeavour to treat the real disease. Let go of the proximate cause. You owe it to yourself.

- Make up your mind not to loathe or discriminate against obese people, starting from today!
- Carbohydrates are fattening. Avoid bad carbs.

CHECKLIST

- Eat less, move more; a complete faux.
- We were not always obsessed with calories.
- Specific foods cause weight gain, not excess calories.
- Sugar kills!

CHAPTER 2: INHERITING OBESITY

It is an undeniable fact that obesity does run in some families. In many cases, obese kids have siblings who are obese as well. In addition, many obese children grow up to become obese adults. As a matter of fact, there is a two hundred to four hundred per cent chance that an obese child will end up obese, even as an adult. There is a controversy that surround this however, and it is centered around the trend of obesity being genetic or environmental, i.e., a nature problem, or an issue of how the child was nurtured.

There are many characteristics that families share which can result in obesity. It is however important to note that obesity became widespread from the 1970s. And while genetics are capable of explaining why inter-individual risks of obesity exists, genetics cannot account for obesity in an entire population.

Because family members live and dwell in the same space, exposed to the same environmental factors, live and lead the same kind of lifestyles, there are huge chances that their exposure to chemicals known as obeso-gens can cause obesity to run in such families. The world we now live in is also blamed and considered toxic, especially because it encourages eating, and discourage physical exertion. Ever since the 1970s, eating habits have changed drastically, as many now eat out, eat food low in fat and high in carbohydrate, eat more on a daily basis and a host of other factors. All of these factors play a party in contributing to the obeso-genic environment. As a result, many of the theories that teach about obesity today discount the place of genetics, and insist that excess calorie consumption leads to obesity.

In a recent research conducted between adoptive parents and their kids, and the biological parents of the adoptees, it was discovered that there was no relationship whatsoever between the weight of adoptive parents and their wards, regardless of whether they were thin or fat, or the environment they provided. This finding was an eye-opener. To a large extent, modern theories had blamed environmental and human factors like dietary habits, junk food, fast food, poor exercise habits, e.t.c., for obesity. Sadly, all of these play no role. As a matter of fact, the fattest adoptees had the thinnest adoptive parents.

However, when the adoptees were compared against their biological parents, there was a strong, consistent correlation between their weights. In this case, the biological parents had very little to do with their kids; neither did they teach them nutritional values or attitudes towards exercise. Despite these, the children tilted strongly towards obesity, like their biological parents. In fact, if an obese child was taken away from obese parents, and put into a thin household, the child still became obese.

Another means by which environmental and genetic factors were distinguished was in a research conducted by Dr. Stunkard in 1991. Here, sets of identical and fraternal twins were examined. These twins were compared under both conditions of being reared apart and together. The comparison of their weights would determine the effect of the different environments. And just as it was in the previous research, the results of this study were shocking as well. It was revealed that about seventy per cent of the variance in obesity is familial. This means that a seventy percent tendency to gain weight is determined by your parentage, and therefore leads us to conclude that obesity is a largely inherited disease.

On an immediate level however, it is clear that inheriting obesity is not the reason for its widespread epidemic nature. Most of the obesity epidemic became visible in the space of one generation, and within that time span, our genes have not changed.

LESSONS AND TAKEAWAYS

- Obesity is highly inherited.
- Obese children often grow up to become obese adults.
- Environmental cues and human behaviors play no role in causing obesity.
- Seventy percent of your tendency to gain weight is determined by your parentage.

QUESTIONS

1. Take a good look at your body structure. Now think deeply about those of your parents. Are you just like them?

   ____

   ____

2. Again, take a good look at your body structure. Now think deeply about those of your siblings. Are you just like them?

   ____

   ____

3. Is obesity a genetic or an environmental problem? Air your opinion whilst providing reasons for your choice.

4. Do you consider obesity a caloric imbalance? Give reasons for your choice.

5. The thrifty gene hypothesis fails to capture obesity. What do you think the real issue is?

ACTION STEPS

- There are other factors beyond inherited factors that account for obesity.
- Food shortage never prevented obesity.

CHECKLIST

- Childhood obesity is a high risk of adult obesity. Watch out!

- A huge percentage of the variance in obesity is familial.
- The thrifty-gene hypothesis is false.

PART 2: THE CALORIE DECEPTION

CHAPTER 3: THE CALORIE-REDUCTION ERROR

In the traditional sense of things, obesity has been viewed as a measure of how humans process calories. In other words, you could measure a person's weight by simply calculating the calories they take in and subtracting the calories they give out. Whatever is left of this is body fat. This equation, regardless of how detailed and true it sounds, is highly deceptive and is what I describe as the calorie deception. Not only is it deceptive, it is dangerous as well. It is dangerous because it is built on so many false assumptions. The first of these assumptions is that calories in and out are dependent of each other. This is a very crucial mistake, and over time, research, experience and experiments have proven this assumption untrue. The truth is that both caloric intake and expenditure are closely dependent variables. Hence, a decrease in the level of caloric intake causes a decrease in the level of calories given out. As a matter of fact, a thirty per cent decrease in caloric intake equals a thirty per cent reduction in caloric expenditure. At the end of this, the result is minimal weight loss.

The second assumption says that basal metabolic rate is stable. We spend so much time obsessing about caloric intake, but hardly pay any attention to caloric expenditure, except for exercise. It is easy to measure the amount of caloric intake, but measuring the amount of caloric expenditure isn't as easy. Hence, the error that we continue to make is that energy expenditure remains constant, excluding exercise. To calculate total energy expenditure, one must sum up basal metabolic rate, thermogenic effect of food, non-exercise activity thermogenesis, excess post-exercise oxygen consumption, and finally, exercise. The total energy expenditure can increase or reduce by a whopping 50 per cent, depending on how much caloric intake the individual is exposed to, as well as a host of other factors.

Another assumption that we've been wrongly fed for so long a time is that we exert conscious control over calories that we take in. Eating is voluntary, and so, we assume that eating is conscious decision, and hence, hunger plays a very minute role in it. However, lots of hormonal systems actually influence the decision of when to eat and when to stop. We make a conscious decision to eat while responding to hunger signals, which are borne out of a hormonal mediation. Consciously, we stop eating when the body sends signals of fullness, also borne out of a hormonal mediation. For instance, when frying food at lunch time, the smell makes you hungry. However, when filled up, the same smell may cause you to be uneasy. Same smell, different decisions. Hence, these decisions are not mainly hormonal. This is the deal. The body is wired in such a way that there exists a system which guides us whether or not to eat. Regulation of body fat is an automatic activity, just like breathing is. Hence, we do not have to remind our bodies to undertake these tasks. The only way we can gain control over this is to have homeostatic mechanisms. Hence, obesity is not a caloric disorder, but a hormonal disorder.

The assumption that fat stores are essentially unregulated is another fallacy that has gone round. Truth is that every single system of the human body is regulated. Hormones such as growth hormone, insulin, e.t.c. regulate growth and blood sugars. However, we are told that the growth of fat cells is essentially unregulated, and that by simply eating, without hormonal interference, fat growth occurs. This is highly untrue, and has been proved so. Every time, new hormonal pathways in the regulation of fat growth continue to be discovered. The best known hormone for regulating fat growth is leptin, but other hormones like lipoprotein lipase, adiponectin and a host of others also play vital roles. If hormones therefore regulate the growth of fat, then it is safe to conclude that obesity is a hormonal disorder, and not a caloric disorder.

The last of the assumptions is the most dangerous of them all. It wrongly states that a calorie is a calorie. While this is true, the real question remains whether or not all calories are equally likely to cause fat gain. You see, the statement that holds that a calorie is a calorie simply implies that when considering weight gain, the only important thing to be considered is the total caloric intake, and thus, all foods can be reduced to their caloric energy. However, one thing to consider is this: will a calorie of sugar cause the same metabolic response as a calorie of olive oil? The answer is clear. No, they won't elicit the same response. Hence, all of these assumptions that concern caloric reduction theory of weight loss have all been proved false, and not all calories are equally likely to cause weight gain.

A calorie refers to a unit of energy, and all of the foods we eat contain calories. Food first enters the stomach from where it moves into the small intestine. As the food journeys through the small and large intestines, nutrients are extracted, and the remnants left as stool. Proteins are then broken down into amino acids; fats are absorbed into the body while carbohydrates provide caloric energy for the body. They all differ in their metabolic processing, resulting in different hormonal stimuli.

LESSONS AND TAKEAWAYS

- The 'Calories in- Calories out= body fat' equation is untrue. It is pure deception.
- Basal metabolic rate does not remain constant.
- We do not exert conscious control the calories we take in, as there are several hormones that influence our decisions of when to eat and when to stop.
- All the systems in the body are regulated, including fat stores.
- All calories are not equally likely to cause weight gain.

QUESTIONS

1. What do you understand calories to mean?

____

____

____

____

2. Have you ever paid attention to your basal metabolic rate? How does it affect your system?

____

____

____

____

3. Having realized that several hormones decide when you eat and when you stop, do you think that you are in control of the calories you take in? Give reasons for your answer.

____

____

____

____

____

____

____

4. Do you consider obesity a function of how people process calories or not? Why?

____

____

____

____

5. If the caloric intake of sugar differs from that of olive oil, what does this imply?

____

____

____

____

ACTION STEPS

- Accept that obesity is not a caloric disorder.

- Don't get worked up over calories. There are no associations between increased caloric consumption and weight gain.
- Calories are essential!

CHECKLIST

- Understand that a decrease in the amount of calories taken in would result in a decrease in the calories put out.
- There is a complex system within the body which guides our decision to eat, or not.
- Calorie reduction is not the main thing involved in weight loss.

CHAPTER 4: THE EXERCISE MYTH

Up until a time like this, we have been taught that caloric imbalance is responsible for obesity. Caloric imbalance refers to an increase in caloric intake shared with a decrease in the level of caloric expenditure, and this has to a large extent has been blamed as the reason for obesity. We have often assumed that by increasing the amount of exercises that we engage in, we can burn off the excess calories that we eat.

Of course, exercise has amazing benefits on our health. As a matter of fact, early Greek physicians concluded that if every individual had the right amount of nourishment and exercise, the safest way to health would have been discovered. As the years went by, a growing concern about heart disease, interest in physical activity and exercise began to grow. Soon after, outfits were set up, advocating that by increasing physical activity, you have better shots at losing weight. Books like 'The Complete Book of Running" became best sellers. And despite the fact that the author died at fifty-two from a massive heart attack, it did very little to set the cause backwards. It was only a matter of years before a new book titled "The New Aerobics" took over the scene. And before one could say jack, tons of physical activity became incorporated into people's leisure times.

The reasonable thing to expect was a fall in obesity rates, as the rates of exercise peaked up. However, the reverse was the case. Regardless of how much money the governments of different nations pumped into promoting exercise for weight loss, it had no effect whatsoever on obesity. None at all. As a matter of fact, obesity increased without relenting. In many American states, exercise increased. However, here's what we found out: increasing the level of exercise did not reduce obesity. While certain states exercised more, others exercised less. And obesity increased by the same amount, regardless.

Another question to consider is if exercise is important in reducing childhood obesity. And the answer is No. According to a research conducted in 2013, physical activities of children aged between three and five were compared against their weight. At the end of the investigation, results revealed that there was no association whatsoever between activity and obesity.

What then is wrong? Central to the calories in and out theory is the idea that physical activity plays a major role in the obesity plague. This idea continually drowns us, reminding us that we once used to walk, but now we drive. And with the use of cars, our exercise lifestyles have reduced, causing us to become obese. The introduction of computers, television sets and video games are all believed to contribute to a sedentary lifestyle. And like any of the others, this seems to make perfect sense. Except that like them all, it's untrue.

According to a research conducted by Dr. Herman Pontzer, it was discovered that the Hadza in Tanzania, burn on a daily basis the same amount of calories as do typical adults in Europe and the United States. Mind you, these people are a hunter-gatherer society with a primitive lifestyle who travel between 15 and 20 miles per day to gather food. Yet, their caloric expenditure remains the same as those of typical adults in Europe and the United States, regardless of the amount of physical activity they engage in.

This is the fact. From time immemorial, exercise rates have not decreased. Sadly, obesity has continually gone ahead in full force. In fact, there is a huge likelihood that a decrease in exercise had any role to play in causing obesity. And if the absence of exercise was not responsible for the obesity epidemic, exercise would most likely not reverse it.

The amount of calories expended on a daily basis is better summed up as the amount of energy you expend. The total energy you expend is an addition of your basal metabolic rate, the thermogenic effect of food, non-exercise activity thermogenesis, excess post exercise oxygen consumption and exercise. Hence, it is important to note that the total energy expenditure is not the same thing as simply exercise. As a matter of fact, the majority if what makes up total energy expenditure isn't exercise, but the basal metabolic rate which involves tasks such as breathing, maintaining body temperature, maintaining vital organs, brain function, liver and kidney function, etc.

The basal metabolic rate depends on many factors, among which are genetics, gender, age, weight, height, diet, body temperature, organ function, etc. exercise on the one hand, is not as effective as we think in the treatment of obesity. Hence, in order for us to reduce obesity, we need to pay attention to what makes us obese. And by continually spending all of our resources on exercise, we are getting drained of the resources needed to actually fight obesity.

LESSONS AND TAKEAWAYS

- Exercise possesses great health benefits. However, in the weight loss region, it is highly limited.
- Exercise is unimportant in the reduction of childhood obesity.
- Total energy expenditure and exercise are two different concepts.

QUESTIONS

1. In a bid to lose weight, have you tried exercising?

____

____

____

2. If your response to (1) above was yes, how did that go? Was it effective? What results were achieved?

____

____

____

____

3. What compensation did you have for exercising?

____

____

____

____

4. If your response to (1) above was no, why haven't you made a move to lose weight by exercising?

____

____

____

____

5. Knowing how limited exercise is in the weight loss journey, what changes do you intend to make to your routine? Write them out.

____

____

____

____

ACTION STEPS

- To reduce obesity, focus on what makes people obese. Not exercise.

CHECKLIST

- Because exercise is not the cause of the obesity epidemic, exercise will not reverse it.
- Weight loss is not among the many benefits of exercise.
- Caloric intake increases in response to exercise

CHAPTER 5: THE OVERFEEDING PARADOX

For more than ten years, Sam Feltham has worked in the U.K. health and fitness industry. He failed to accept the caloric reduction theory, and took it upon himself to prove it false. He made a decision to consume five thousand, seven hundred and ninety-four calories on a daily basis. These calories consisted of low-carbohydrate, high fat diet of natural foods. He believed mainly that refined carbohydrates caused weight gain, not total calories. At the end of his experiment, he gained only 1.3 kilograms, while still dropping more than an inch from his waist measurement. Hence, he did gain weight, but it was lean mass. Mind you, according to the regular caloric calculation, he should have gained nothing less than 7.3 kilograms.

Following this, Feltham embarked on yet another experiment. This time around, he consumed five thousand, seven hundred and ninety three calories of a standard American diet with lots of highly processed fake foods. He followed a breakdown which was very much in line with the U.S dietary guidelines. At the end of this experiment, Feltham had gained 7.1 kilograms, which was very similar to what the calorie formula predicted. His waist size shot up by an additional 3.6 inches.

All of these occurred in the same person. He consumed pretty much the same caloric intake, yet the different diets produced very different results. This goes to show that beyond calories, there is a greater force at work, and that diet composition also plays a huge role in all of these. The paradox therefore suggests that excessive caloric consumption does not necessarily translate to weight gain- a stance that contradicts the caloric reduction theory.

We can test the hypothesis that suggests that eating too much causes obesity. To find this out, all you have to do is get a group of volunteers, overfeed them and document the result. If the hypothesis is true, obesity should be the end result. Experiments like these have been carried out. One of them was performed by Ethan Sims in the late 1960s. He began by trying to force mice to gain weight. But despite all that he did, they only ate to become full, and after that, they would eat no more. They would not become obese. And even when they were forcefully fed, their metabolism increased as well, so no weight was gained. Dissatisfied with the results, he decided to carry out the test on humans. Is it possible that one could deliberately make humans gain weight?

To find answers to this question, he recruited college students. He encouraged them to eat as much as they wanted, whatever and whenever, all in a bid to gain weight. Yet, regardless of his expectations, they did not become obese. As a matter of fact, he discovered that it was no easy task getting people to gain weight.

He didn't relent, but changed course instead. Next up, Dr. Sims recruited convicts at the Vermont state prison and fed them. Initially, their weights rose. Soon after however, they began to stabilize. They were initially happy about their caloric increase, but as their weights increased, they found it increasingly difficult to overeat. Some of them even dropped out of the study.

Some prisoners were convinced to eat as much as 10000 calories daily. In the course of four to six months, the rest of the prisoners did gain between twenty to twenty five percent of their original body weight. There was a huge variance in the weight gain between persons. It was evident that something was contributing to the vast differences in the weight they gained, but it was not caloric intake or exercise.

It was metabolism. The more the subjects ate, the more their total energy expenditures increased. What happened was that their bodies all tried to burn off the excess calories that they were consuming so as to return to its original weight. Total energy expenditure comprises mainly if basal metabolic rate, and is not constant, but varies in response to caloric intake. Hence, at the end of the experiment, the subjects body weights quickly returned to normal as most of them did not retain any of the weights they gained.

The human body is smart. Increased caloric intake is met with increased caloric expenditure. And if excess calories do not cause weight gain, then reducing calories won't cause weight loss.

LESSONS AND TAKEAWAYS

- Overfeeding is not the cause of obesity, and cannot cause obesity.
- Metabolism is key!
- Excess calories do not cause weight gain; reducing calories will not cause weight loss.

QUESTIONS

1. What do you say about your weight?

____

____

____

____

2. By overfeeding or underfeeding, did you achieve long term weight gain or weight loss results? If yes, describe your experience in detail.

____

____

____

____

3. If your response to (2) above is No, what do you suppose the problem is? Why won't the weight stay, or leave, permanently?

____

____

____

____

4. What do you understand by metabolism?

____

____

____

____

5. Did you notice any change(s) in your body's metabolic structure since you began your weight gain/ weight loss journey? Explain in details.

____

____

____

____

ACTION STEPS

- Understand that metabolism is the means by which your body resets itself to an already set thermostat. You cannot control it.
- Overeating or under-eating should be done away with. They both cannot produce lasting results.

CHECKLIST

- You can only temporarily force your body weight higher than your body wants it to be, and vice versa.
- Homeostasis defends the body set weight against changes, upwards or downwards.
- Obesity has a set point that is too high. This is its problem.

PART 3: A NEW MODEL OF OBESITY

CHAPTER 6: A NEW HOPE

Here's the hidden truth. The caloric-reduction theory of obesity isn't half as useful as we've been made to believe. Over and over again, studies posited that it would not result in a permanent weight loss. And it was either of these two factors: perhaps, patients weren't following it to the letter, or the Eat Less, Move More strategy wasn't as effective as it sounded. It seemed practically impossible for health care personnel to let go of the calorie model. What then was left for them to do? Blame the patient, of course!

Year in, year out, doctors and dieticians laid the blame at the patients' feet, ridiculing and berating them for their inability to resist calories. They dwelt so much on this as it empowered them to look beyond their failures to provide a solution to obesity, and instead pass the blame onto the patient as a lack of willpower and/or laziness. Fortunately for us all, it might take a while, but the truth cannot remain hidden for life. And that is what is happening today. The caloric-reduction model was just wrong. It didn't work. As long as excess calories did not cause obesity, reduced calories could not cure it. Lack of exercise did not cause obesity, so increased exercise could not cure it.

Having exposed the lies surrounding obesity and caloric consumption, a new theory of obesity emerged. This theory provides us all with the much needed hope, reassuring everyone that rational, successful treatments can be employed. It is important to however answer the question: What causes weight gain? In response to this, there are lots of theories that suffice. Some say Calories, others say sugar. Some say refined carbohydrates, others say wheat. The list is endless. And all of these theories fight among themselves, as though they were all mutually exclusive, implying that a single, true cause of obesity exists. For instance, recent research compares low calorie and low carbohydrate diets. This approach is however wrong, as many of these theories in one way or the other, contribute to obesity. Using heart attacks as an example, we realize that contributing factors such as age, sex, diabetes, stress, smoking and a lot more can contribute to having a heart attack. And while some of these factors can be modified, not all of them can. But they all contribute to heart-attack risk. Because they all contribute to a certain degree, then, they are all correct. Nevertheless, they all can be termed incorrect as neither of them is the sole reason for heart attacks.

Another major problem with obesity-centered research is that it fails to accept the time-dependence of the obesity disease. Obesity isn't a one-time thing, but a disease that takes a while to be developed, usually over decades. An average obese patient would have started out being a little overweight as a child, and slowly begins to gain weight on a yearly basis, roughly about 0.5 to 1 kilogram per year. And while this might sound like a small amount of weight to gain in a year, it should be noted that during the space of forty years, the patient would have amassed up to 80 pounds, which equals 35 kilograms.

Considering the amount of time given for obesity to develop, it is irrelevant to embark on short-time studies, as they are highly limited in their use. Let's take a look at this. If one were to study the development of rust in a pipe, and knowing that rusting is a time-dependent process that occurs over months of exposure to moisture, it would make very little sense to look at studies of only one- or two-days' duration. If one were to do the latter, we might as well come to the conclusion that water does not cause pipe rust, since we failed to observe any rust formation in the 48-hour time frame. Sadly, this particular mistake is often repeated when conducting obesity studies. It takes decades for obesity to develop, yet, studies continually consider obesity within the time frame of a year or less. In fact, there are thousands of studies on human obesity whose study lasted less than a week. Still, they all claim to shed light on human obesity.

As it stands, there is no clear, focused, unified theory of obesity, neither is there a framework for understanding weight gain and weight loss. This lack hinders the advancement of research, which brings us to this point- to build the hormonal obesity theory. Obesity is a hormonal dysregulation of fat mass. The body maintains a body set weight, much like a thermostat in a house. When the body set weight is set too high, obesity results. If our current weight is below our body set weight, our body, by stimulating hunger and/or decreasing metabolism, will try to gain weight to reach that body set weight. Thus, excessive eating and slowed metabolism are the result rather than the cause of obesity. But what caused our body set weight to be so high in the first place? This is the same as simply saying: What causes obesity? And in order to answer this, we need to understand how the body set weight is regulated.

Contrary to what many people think, Leptin, a key regulator of body fat, did not turn out to be the main hormone involved in setting the body weight. As a matter of fact, hormones like Ghrelin (the hunger regulating hormone) and peptide YY and cholecystokinin (satiety regulating hormones), all play a role in making you start and stop eating, but they do not appear to affect the body set weight. How do we know? A hormone suspected of causing weight gain must pass the causality test. If we inject this hormone into people, they must gain weight. These hunger and satiety hormones do not pass the causality test, but there are two hormones that do: insulin and cortisol.

LESSONS AND TAKEAWAYS

- The caloric reduction theory resulted in the patients bearing the brunt, due to its infectiveness.
- Caloric reduction theory was wrong. It did not work.
- There is no single, true cause of obesity.
- Obesity is a time-dependent disease.

QUESTIONS

1. Cast your mind back to when you were a little child. Would you describe yourself as being obese, even as a child?

   ____

   ____

2. Have you ever heard of insulin? What do you know about insulin?

   ____

   ____

   ____

   ____

3. What is your consumption of dietary fat on a scale of 1 to 10?

    ____

4. Have you ever tried resisting the urge to eat? How did that work out?

    ____

    ____

    ____

    ____

5. Insulin causes obesity through an effect in the brain. What are your thoughts on this?

    ____

    ____

    ____

    ____

ACTION STEPS

- Understand that obesity develops over time. Reversing it will also take time.
- Obesity is a hormonal imbalance

CHECKLIST

- Lack of exercise does not cause obesity.

CHAPTER 7: INSULIN

If I told you I could actually make anyone fat, would you believe me? That doesn't matter though, because I can. You may wonder how. The answer is simple: by prescribing insulin. You see, after this prescription, it matters less if you are willing, or if you even exercise. Neither will what you choose to eat count. The bottom line is that you'll get fat. And all it takes is enough insulin and enough time.

One constant phenomenon that has been associated with obesity is a high secretion of insulin. As a matter of fact, obese people secrete much higher levels of insulin than do those of normal weight. When compared with lean persons, insulin levels quickly return to baseline after a meal. In obese individuals however, their insulin levels remain elevated. Research has revealed that in obese subjects, insulin levels are almost 20 percent higher and these elevated levels are strongly linked with significant indices like waist circumference and waist/hip ratio. The close association between insulin levels and obesity suggests, but does not prove the causal nature of this relationship.

Measuring insulin levels may be pretty difficult, as a result of the constant rate of insulin level fluctuation on a daily basis in response to food. Measuring an average level is more realistic, but even that requires multiple measurements throughout the day. Fasting insulin levels are a simpler, one-step measurement. It is important to note that studies have revealed that there is a nexus between high fasting insulin levels and obesity, and this relationship becomes even stronger when we consider only a person's fat mass rather than his or her total weight.

In the San Antonio Heart Study, high fasting insulin was tightly correlated to weight gain over eight years of follow up. This relationship is not accidental. Insulin resistance plays a major role in causing obesity. Hence, the relationship between elevated insulin and obesity becomes clearly established. This leads us to finding out whether this association is a causal relationship, or not. In other words; does high insulin cause obesity?

If you take insulin, you will get fat. This is an undeniable fact. More insulin consumption equals more obesity. Insulin causes obesity. Insulin causes weight gain. There are two types of diabetes, and insulin is often used to treat both types. In type 1 diabetes, the insulin-producing cells of the pancreas are destroyed, resulting in very low levels of insulin. In this case, patients require insulin injections to survive. On the other hand, in type 2 diabetes, cells are resistant to insulin and insulin levels are high. Patients do not always require insulin and are often treated first with oral medications.

In a study carried out in 1993, researchers compared a standard dose of insulin to a high dose designed to tightly control blood sugars in type 1 diabetic patients. At the end of six years, the study proved that intensive control of blood sugars resulted in fewer complications for those patients. However, what happened to their weight? Participants in the high-dose group gained, on average 4.5 kilograms more than participants in the standard group. More than 30 per cent of patients experienced significant weight gain! Prior to the study however, both groups were more or less equal in weight, with little obesity. The only difference between the groups was the amount of insulin administered. Were these patients suddenly lacking in willpower? Were they lazier than they had been before the study? Were they more gluttonous? No, no and no. Insulin levels were increased. Patients gained weight. Long-term studies in type 2 diabetes show the same weight-gaining effect of insulin.

Having established that the consumption of insulin results in weight gain, its reduction should also result in weight loss. As insulin is reduced to very low levels, we should expect significant and severe weight loss. A classic instance is the untreated type 1 diabetic patient. Type 1 diabetes is an autoimmune disease that destroys the insulin-producing beta cells of the pancreas. Insulin falls to extremely low levels. Blood sugar increases, but the trademark of this condition is severe weight loss. Today, type 1 diabetic patients are treated by daily injections of insulin.

There are some patients who wish to lose weight for cosmetic reasons. Diabulimia is the deliberate under-dosing of insulin for the purpose of immediate and substantial weight loss. It is extremely dangerous and certainly not advisable. However, the practice persists because it is an extremely effective form of weight loss. Insulin levels go down. Weight is lost.

LESSONS AND TAKEAWAYS

- By prescribing insulin, anyone can become fat.
- Insulin levels are twenty per cent higher in obese subjects.
- Insulin resistance plays a major role in causing obesity.

- Insulin causes obesity!

QUESTIONS

1. If you could gain weight by increasing your insulin consumption, would you?

   ____

   ____

2. If you could lose weight by reducing your insulin consumption, would you?

   ____

   ____

3. Depending on your response to either (1) or (2) above, provide reasons for your choice.

   ____

   ____

   ____

   ____

4. What do you know about leptins?

   ____

   ____

   ____

   ____

5. Knowing that obesity is a hormonal imbalance, do you think it's possible to balance our hormones? Why?

   ____

   ____

   ____

ACTION STEPS

- With insulin infused into or reduced from your diet, exercise will not be necessary. Weight gain or weight loss will be bound to happen.

CHECKLIST

- The more insulin you give, the more obese you get.

CHAPTER 8: CORTISOL

Beyond the use of insulin, I can make you fat by prescribing prednisone, a synthetic version of the human hormone cortisol. Prednisone is often used to treat a wide range of diseases which include asthma, rheumatoid arthritis, inflammatory bowel disease, cancer, e.t.c. the most consistent effect of prednisone, like insulin, is that it makes you fat. Both insulin and cortisol play a major role in carbohydrate metabolism. Prolonged cortisol stimulation will raise glucose levels and, subsequently, insulin. This increase in insulin plays a substantial role in the resulting weight gain.

Cortisol is the so-called stress hormone, which act as a go-between the flight-or-fight response, a set of physiological responses to perceived threats. Cortisol is crucial in preparing our bodies for action—to fight or flee. Once released, cortisol substantially enhances the availability of glucose which provides energy for muscles. All available energy is directed toward surviving the stressful event, while temporarily restricting long-term metabolic activities like digestion.

Proteins are broken down and converted to glucose (gluconeogenesis), and soon after energetic physical exertion follows, burning up these newly available stores of glucose. Shortly thereafter, we were either dead, or the danger was past and our cortisol decreased back to its normal low levels. And that's the point: the body is well adapted to a short-term increase in cortisol and glucose levels.

In the long run, however, a problem comes to be. Cortisol raises insulin at first glance. Both hormones seem to have opposite effects. Insulin is a storage hormone, and the body stores energy in the form of glycogen and fat. Cortisol, on the other hand, prepares the body for action, by moving energy out of stores into easily usable forms like glucose. And although both cortisol and insulin have similar weight gain effects, they each play opposite roles when we're under longterm psychological stress.

In our world today, there are tons of chronic, nonphysical stressors that increase our cortisol levels. These include but are not limited to marital issues, problems at work, arguments with children e.t.c. However, all of these do not result in the vigorous physical exertion needed to burn off the blood glucose. In situations where we get exposed to chronic stress, glucose levels remain high and there is no resolution to the stressor. Our blood glucose can remain elevated for months, triggering the release of insulin. Chronically elevated cortisol leads results in increased insulin levels. Insulin resistance is crucial to the development of obesity, resulting directly in higher insulin levels. Unfortunately, increased insulin levels are a major driver of obesity. Multiple studies confirm that increasing cortisol increases insulin resistance.

If an increase in cortisol raises insulin, a reduction in cortisol should lower it. This was observed to be true in transplant patients who take prednisone for years or decades as part of their anti-rejection medication. Results from one of the studies revealed that weaning them off prednisone resulted in a twenty five percent drop in plasma insulin, which is equal to a six percent weight loss and a 7.7 percent decrease in waist girth.

LESSONS AND TAKEAWAYS

- By prescribing prednisone, anyone can become fat.
- Cortisol is an essential hormone when preparing the body for action.
- Cortisol enhances glucose availability.
- Cortisol raises insulin, and causes weight gain!

QUESTIONS

1. Cortisol and insulin play similar roles, in the long-term. How does this affect the human body?

   ____

   ____

   ____

   ____

2. Does excess cortisol lead to weight gain?

   ____

   ____

3. How do you reduce stress? Do you consider this an important 'task?'

   ____

   ____

   ____

   ____

4. What methods of stress relief do you employ?

5. How well do you sleep? Are you sleep deprived?

ACTION STEPS

- Have proper night rests.

CHECKLIST

- Sleep deprivation and weight gain are connected.

CHAPTER 9: THE ATKINS ONSLAUGHT

Having understood that insulin causes obesity, we seek to find out the foods that cause our insulin levels to rise or to spike. Most glaring on the list is the refined carbohydrate which consists of highly refined grains and sugars. Long ago, William Banting said that fattening carbohydrates were responsible for causing obesity.

The most notorious foods known for increasing blood sugars are highly refined carbohydrates. High blood sugars lead to high insulin levels. High insulin levels lead to weight gain and obesity. This cycle, made up of causes and effects has become known as the carbohydrate-insulin hypothesis. This controversy was centered around Dr. Robert Atkins. In 1963, Dr. Robert Atkins was a fat man. Like William Banting 100 years before, he needed to do something. Weighing in at 224 pounds (100 kilograms), he had recently begun his cardiology practice in New York City. He had tried the conventional ways to lose weight, but had met with no success. Recalling the medical literature published by Drs. Pennington and Gordon on low-carbohydrate diets, he decided to try the low-carbohydrate approach himself. To his amazement, it worked as advertised. Without counting calories, he shed his bothersome extra weight. He started prescribing the low-carbohydrate diet to patients and had some notable success.

The doctor never laid any claim to the invention of the low-carb diet. In all truth, that approach had been around for quite a while, before he wrote about it. Jean Anthelme Brillat-Savarin had written about carbohydrates and obesity in 1825. In similar fashion, William

Banting had described the same relationship in his bestselling pamphlet, Letter on Corpulence, in 1863. By the mid 1950s however, the caloric-reduction theory of obesity was gaining relevance. Discussions centered around calories, rather than food, seemed to make more scientific sense. Yet, there were still holdouts. Dr. Alfred Pennington wrote an editorial in the New England Journal of Medicine in 1953 emphasizing the role of carbohydrates in obesity. Studies conducted by Dr. Walter Bloom which compared low-carbohydrate diets to fasting regimens had found comparable weight loss between the two. In 1967, Dr. Irwin Stillman wrote The Doctor's Quick Weight Loss Diet where he recommended a high-protein, low-carbohydrate diet. The book sold in millions. It was assumed that if it required extra energy to metabolize dietary protein, eating more protein could theoretically cause more weight loss. In fact, Dr. Stillman himself lost fifty pounds following the "Stillman diet," which contained up to 90 percent protein. He reportedly used the diet to treat more than 10,000 overweight patients.

By the time Dr. Atkins joined the fray, the low-carbohydrate revolution was already well underway. Dr. Atkins argued that by drastically reducing the consumption of carbohydrates, insulin levels would be kept low, causing a reduction in hunger which would eventually lead to weight loss. Shortly after, however, the national authorities responded by publishing a blistering attack on Atkins's ideas. At the time, many physicians expressed concern over the high fat content of the diet, which they feared would lead to heart attacks and strokes. Nonetheless, low-carb proponents continued to preach.

In 1983, Dr. Richard Bernstein, a type 1 diabetic since age nine, opened a contentious clinic to treat diabetics with a strict low-carbohydrate diet, a method that directly contradicted most nutritional and medical teachings of the time. Dr. Bernstein's Diabetes Solution was published in 1997, and on two different occasions, Atkins updated his bestseller with the publication of Dr. Atkins' New Diet Revolution. Soon enough, both Bernstein's and Atkins's books became bestsellers, selling over 10 million copies. Following this feat, Rachael and Richard Heller wrote The Carbohydrate Addict's Diet in 1993, which sold more than 6 million copies. The Atkins onslaught had come to stay. This model, rekindled in the 1990s, ignited into a full-scale inferno in 2002 when award-winning journalist Gary Taubes wrote a controversial lead article in the New York Times entitled "What If It's All Been a Big Fat Lie?" arguing that dietary fat was actually quite harmless to human health. He followed that up with the best-selling books Good Calories, Bad Calories and Why We Get Fat, in which he expounded on the idea that carbohydrates were the root cause of weight gain.

LESSONS AND TAKEWAWAYS

- Refined carbohydrates are responsible for the rise in our insulin levels.
- Low fat diet slows body metabolism the most.
- Refined carbs are easy to become addicted to.
- The toxicity of refined carbohydrates lie in its processing.

QUESTIONS

1. List ten highly refined carbohydrates that you know.

2. Do you understand the carbohydrate-insulin hypothesis?

3. What was spectacular about the Atkins diet? What did it take into consideration that the others failed at?

4. Eating refined carbohydrates may cause food addictions. Any experience?

____

____

5. What made the carbohydrate-insulin hypothesis incomplete?

____

____

____

____

ACTION STEPS

- Sugar plays a crucial role in obesity.
- High carbohydrate intake may not always be the main cause of high insulin levels.

CHECKLIST

- The carbohydrate-insulin hypothesis is incomplete.

CHAPTER 10: INSULIN RESISTANCE: THE MAJOR PLAYER

For several decades, the famous Oprah Winfrey has waged her weight loss battles publicly. At her heaviest, she weighed 107.5 kilograms. And by the year 2005, she was weighing 72.6 kilograms. She was excited, as she cut down on carbohydrates, had her exercise done regularly, had a personal chef and a trainer. Seemingly, she had done all that she needed to do, and done them all right. But by 2009, she gained another 18 kilograms. Why? Why was it so difficult to keep the weight off? Why is long-standing obesity so difficult to treat?

You see, time dependence in obesity is almost universally understood but rarely acknowledged. Usually, obesity occurs over a period of time. Gradually, the individual gains 0.5 to 1 kilogram on a yearly basis. Within a twenty five year time frame, the individual would have gained 23 kilograms. Persons, who have been obese, all of their life begin to find it an excruciating task to lose weight. Similarly, people with recent weight gain have a much, much easier time dropping the excess weight. In the conventional caloric system, it is largely assumed that losing 4.5 kilograms equals the same experience for everyone, regardless of how long you've been overweight, and that by simply reducing the calories, you'll do away with the weight. But this is untrue.

What matters a lot here is the timeframe in which the individual has been obese. Yeah, many try to downplay its effects, but the idea that long-standing obesity is much more difficult to treat has the stench of truth. It is important therefore that we acknowledge the phenomenon of time dependence. As early as seventeen years of age, obesity has consequences that reach far into the future. And any comprehensive theory of obesity must be able to explain why its duration matters so much.

High insulin levels cause weight gain. Food choices play a role in raising insulin levels. But we continue to leave out a major channel via which insulin is increased, one that is both time dependent and independent of diet: insulin resistance. Insulin resistance is the hidden force behind most of modern medicine's archenemies, including obesity, diabetes, fatty liver, Alzheimer's disease, heart disease, cancer, high blood pressure and high cholesterol.

The human body is illustrated by the fundamental biological principle of homeostasis. Should things change in one direction, the body reacts by changing in the opposite direction to return closer to its original state. In an event that we become very cold, the body tries to adapt by increasing body-heat generation, and vice versa. For human survival, adaptability is a necessary attribute, which holds true for all biological systems. In other words, the body develops resistance. The body resists change out of its comfort range by adapting to it.

In the case of insulin resistance, what happens? When insulin no longer fits into the receptor, the cell is called insulin resistant. And as a result of this, less glucose enters. The cell senses that there is too little glucose inside. Instead, glucose is piling up on its outside. Having beings starved of glucose, the cell demands more. And in a bid to compensate for the starvation, the body produces extra insulin. Mind you, the fit is still poor, but more channels are opened, allowing a normal amount of glucose to enter. As we develop insulin resistance, our bodies increase our insulin levels to get the same result which is glucose in the cell. But we pay very heavily for this by having constantly elevated insulin levels. And the consequence is that insulin resistance leads to high insulin levels, and high insulin levels in turn cause obesity.

In the very first place, note that the insulin resistance was caused by the receptor. You see, insulin is the same hormone, whether found in an obese or a lean person. Hence, the problem of insulin resistance lies with the receptor. The insulin receptor failed to respond properly, locking the glucose out of the cell.

LESSONS AND TAKEAWAYS

- Long-standing obesity is difficult to treat.
- Time-dependence in obesity is hardly acknowledged.
- Reducing the calories does not equal losing the weight.
- Insulin resistance- a force to reckon with!

QUESTIONS

1. How does the human body develop resistance?

   ____

   ____

   ____

   ____

2. In what manner does insulin birth insulin resistance?

3. Large doses of insulin and insulin resistance. What is the correlation here?

4. In your opinion; which came first: High insulin resulting in insulin resistance, or the other way around? Provide reasons for your choice.

5. Of what use is exercise on insulin sensitivity, in the muscles?

ACTION STEPS

- Persistence creates resistance.
- Practice eating full meals daily, whilst avoiding snacks.

CHECKLIST

- The eat more, weigh less theory does not work!

PART 4: THE SOCIAL PHENOMENON OF OBESITY

CHAPTER 11: BIG FOOD, MORE FOOD AND THE NEW SCIENCE OF DIABESITY

In a bid to make more money, Big Food companies decided to fuel the increase in eating opportunities. This, they achieved by creating an entirely new category of food, called "snack food," and promoted it persistently. They made advertisements available on diverse platforms: TV, print, radio and Internet alike. However, there is a more subtle form of advertising known sponsorship and research. Big Food sponsors a lot of large nutritional organizations and medical associations.

In 1988, the American Heart Association decided to accept cash to put its Heart Check symbol on foods of otherwise dubious nutritional quality. According to research, in 2002, the American Heart Association received over two million dollars from this program alone. Food companies paid as much as seven thousand, five hundred dollars for products ranging from one to nine, but there was a volume discount for more than twenty-five products. Exclusive deals were, of course, more expensive. As at 2009, foods such as Cocoa Puffs and Frosted Mini Wheats were still on the Heart Check list. The 2013 Dallas Heart Walk organized by the American Heart Association featured Frito-Lay as a prominent sponsor. Even in Canada, the same was being done. A bottle of grape juice proudly bearing the Health Check contained ten teaspoons of sugar. The single fact that these foods contained pure sugar seemed to be of no concern to anyone.

A lot of health professionals endorse the use of artificial meal-replacement shakes or bars, drugs and surgery as evidence-based diet aids. Let's consider the makeup of a popular meal-replacement shake: water, corn maltodextrin, sugar, milk, protein concentrate and canola oil. This sickening blend of water, sugar and canola oil does not really meet my definition of healthy.

In addition to the aforementioned, impartiality or a lack of it can pose a serious when it comes to publishing medical and health information. In some papers published in journals and the web, the financial-disclosures section can run for more than half a page. This is where it gets interesting. Funding sources affect study results, greatly. Let's take a look at a study conducted in 2007. The study particularly examined soft drinks. According to the results, Dr. David Ludwig from Harvard University discovered that accepting funds from companies whose products are reviewed increased the chances of a favorable result by roughly 700 percent! Similarly, Marion Nestle, professor of nutrition and food studies at New York University agreed with this result, concluding in 2011 that it is difficult to find studies that did not come to conclusions favoring the sponsor's commercial interest. What had happened? Big Food had been allowed to infiltrate the hallowed halls of medicine because of what they offered the health companies. They pushed fructose, obesity drugs, artificial meal replacement shakes and a host of others. However, it became increasingly difficult to ignore the looming obesity epidemic, and a culprit had to be blamed for it. In this case, calories bore the brunt. And they began to advocate the consumption of fewer calories, while advising more consumption of every other thing. But let's face it: No company sells Calories, neither is there a brand or food called Calories. Calories, without a face of their own began to take all of the blame. According to them, candies won't make you fat, instead, calories will. They say that a hundred calories of cola is just as likely as a hundred calories of broccoli to make you fat. They say that a calorie is a calorie. Sadly thought, I'm yet to see a single person that grew fat by eating too much steamed broccoli.

The truth is this: we cannot continue consuming our usual diet and add some fat or protein or snacks and expect to lose weight. It is totally illogical to suggest that one could achieve weight-loss by eating more. When they say: eat six times a day, eat high protein, eat more vegetables, eat more omega 3s, eat more fiber, eat more vitamins, eat more snacks, eat low fat, eat breakfast, and so on and so forth, they simply want to keep making money. If not, why else would anyone give such unintelligent advice? The fat is this: nobody makes any money when you eat less. By consuming more supplements, the supplement companies make money. If you drink more milk, the dairy farmers make money. If you eat more breakfast, the breakfast-food companies make money. If you eat more snacks, the snack companies make money. The list is endless. And the most stupid myth is that eating more frequently causes weight loss. It is really stupid!

LESSONS AND TAKEAWAYS

- Snack food was created mainly to fuel the increase in eating opportunities.
- Commercial interest became the order of the day.
- Calories became the perfect scapegoat.
- Eating frequently as a means of losing weight was a commercial strategy.
- You cannot feed on snacks to lose weight.

QUESTIONS

1. Do you believe that snacking will make you thin? Provide reasons for your response.

____

____

____

____

2. What is your opinion on breakfast and whether or not to skip it?

____

____

____

____

3. For how long have you forced yourself to eat breakfast, even when you didn't feel like it? And why?

____

____

____

____

4. If you were told to eat more fruits and vegetables, would you?

____

____

5. Are you willing to replace unhealthier foods in your diets with fruits and vegetables, and not just adding to them?

____

____

ACTION STEPS

- You do not have to eat breakfast. It is not necessary.
- Consume more fruits and vegetables.

CHECKLIST

- Insulin not only causes obesity, it causes type 2 diabetes as well.

CHAPTER 12: POVERTY AND OBESITY

In Atlanta, there is a Center for Disease Control which does a good job with keeping detailed statistics about the prevalence of obesity in the United States, which differs remarkably between regions. Also, states with the least records of obesity in 2010 have higher rates than those that were found in states with the most obesity in 1990. On the overall, there has been a huge increase in obesity in the United States.

Regardless of the similarity between the U.S and Canadian culture and genetics, U.S rates of obesity are much higher. This suggests that a role is being played by government policies in the development of obesity. For instance, states like Texas tend to have much more obesity than states like California and Colorado. For a long time, socioeconomic status has been known to play a role in the development of obesity. This simply implies that there is a strong connection between poverty and obesity. It has been discovered that the poorest states have the most obese people. With a 2013 median income of $39,031 Mississippi is the poorest state in the U.S, yet it has the highest level of obesity, at 35.4 percent.

How is poverty connected to obesity? A theory of obesity exists, known as the food-reward hypothesis. According to this theory, the rewarding quality of the food causes overeating. Perhaps, because food is more enjoyable than it has ever been, obesity rates have increased by causing people to eat more. Rewards reinforce behavior, and the behavior of eating is rewarded by the palatability, the deliciousness of the food. Mind you, this increased palatability of food is not accidental. As a result of societal changes, more meals are being eaten away from the home, at restaurants and fast-food outlets. Many of the foods prepared in those places are designed in such a way that they appear hyper-palatable through the use of chemicals, additives and other artificial processes. The addition of sugar and seasonings may trick the taste buds into believing that the food is more rewarding. This position is supported in books such as Sugar, Salt and Fat: How the Food Giants Hooked Us, by Michael Moss, and The End of Overeating: Taking Control of the Insatiable American Appetite by David Kessler. By including added sugars, salt and fat to our diet, this combination bears a lopsided amount of blame for inducing us to overeat. But the truth remains that people have been eating salt, sugar and fat for the last 5000 years.

In all honesty, all of these are not new additions to the human diet. Ice cream has been a summertime treat for over 100 years. Same as Chocolate bars, cookies, cakes and sweets. Long before, in the 1950s, children enjoyed their Oreo cookies in the 1950s without the problem of obesity. Hence, the crux of this argument is that food is more delicious in 2010 than in 1970 because food scientists engineer it to be so. As a result, we cannot help but overeat calories and therefore become obese. The implication is that hyper-palatable fake foods are more delicious and more rewarding than real foods, but it's pretty difficult to believe this. I mean, would you choose a fake highly processed food over fresh salmon sashimi dipped in soy sauce with wasabi, claiming that the former is more delicious? I'd say No. Yet, the association of obesity with poverty presents a problem.

The food-reward hypothesis opines that obesity should be more prevalent among the rich, since they can afford to buy more of the highly rewarding foods. However, the reverse is the case. Lower-income groups suffer more obesity. Truth is, while the rich can afford to buy food that is both rewarding and expensive, the poor can afford only rewarding food that is cheaper. Steak and lobster are both rewarding and expensive. Likewise restaurant meals. And despite the huge difference in daily physical activity, obesity rates are higher in the less affluent but more physically active group. Neither food reward nor physical exertion can explain the association between obesity and poverty.

So what drives obesity in the poor? It is the same thing that drives obesity everywhere else: refined carbohydrates. For those dealing with poverty, food needs to be affordable. Some dietary fats are quite inexpensive. Dietary proteins, such as meat and dairy, tend to be relatively expensive. Less expensive vegetable proteins, such as tofu or legumes, are available but not typical in a North American diet. This leaves carbohydrates. If refined carbohydrates are significantly cheaper than other sources of food, then those living in poverty will eat refined carbohydrates.

LESSONS AND TAKEAWAYS.

- Socioeconomic status plays a major role in the development of obesity.
- States with the most poverty tend to have the highest obesity.
- The Food-reward hypothesis: the link between obesity and poverty.
- Obesity is not the result of a modern lifestyle.

QUESTIONS

1. What role is being played by government policies in the development of obesity?

   ____

   ____

   ____

   ____

2. Why is poverty linked to obesity?

   ____

   ____

   ____

   ____

3. How logical is the food-reward hypothesis?

   ____

   ____

   ____

   ____

4. Highly refined carbohydrates and obesity. Correlate these two in the light of poverty.

   ____

   ____

ACTION STEPS

- Obesity, concentrated among the poor is driven by refined carbohydrates, being the most affordable food category.

CHECKLIST

- Neither food, nor physical exertion can explain the correlation between obesity and poverty.

CHAPTER 13: CHILDHOOD OBESITY

As the years rolled by, the alarming rise of obesity and Type 2 diabetes in school-aged children resulted in the deployment of hundreds of millions of dollars for a counterattack. The first approach taken was the Eat Less, Move More approach, which sported a perfect record untarnished by success. However, upon carrying out some research, it was discovered that the weight-loss strategy was virtually useless.

Between 1977 and 2000, childhood obesity hit the rooftops, as it doubled and tripled across children in different age categories. Gradually, diseases such as type 2 diabetes and high blood pressure, became common amongst kids. Childhood obesity also leads to adult obesity and future health problems, particularly cardiovascular issues. Overweight children who became normal weight as adults have the same mortality risk as those who have never been overweight.

Obesity is considered an energy-balance problem, one of eating too much or exercising too little. Since six-month-olds eat on demand and are often breastfed, it is impossible that they eat too much. Since six-month-olds do not walk, it is impossible that they exercise too little. Similarly, birth weight has increased by as much as half a pound (200 grams) over the last twenty-five years. The newborn cannot eat too much or exercise too little. What is going on here? Numerous hypotheses have been offered to explain newborn obesity. One popular theory suggests that certain chemicals (obesogens) in our modern environment lead to obesity, chemicals that disrupt the normal functional hormonal systems of the body. Since obesity is a hormonal rather than a caloric imbalance, this notion does make some intuitive sense.

Insulin is the major hormonal driver of weight gain, and is responsible for adult obesity. Insulin causes newborn, infant and childhood obesity. One might wonder where an infant would get high insulin levels from. The answer is clear: From his or her mother. According to a recent research conducted by Dr. David Ludwig where he examined the relationship between the weights of 513,501 women and their 1,164,750 offspring, increased maternal weight gain is strongly associated with increased neonatal weight gain. This is solely because both mother and fetus share the same blood supply. As a result, any hormonal imbalances of which high insulin levels is inclusive, are automatically and directly transmitted through the placenta from the mother to the growing fetus.

When fetuses are large for their gestational age, they are referred to as Fetal macrosomia. A number of risk factors surround these fetuses, but the most prominent ones are maternal gestational diabetes, maternal obesity and maternal weight gain. All of these conditions have one thing in common: High maternal levels of insulin. The high levels transmit to the developing fetus, resulting in one that is too large. As a consequence, too much insulin in the newborn results in the development of insulin resistance, which leads to even higher levels of insulin in a classic vicious cycle. The high insulin levels produce obesity in the newborn as well as the six-month-old infant. The origins of both infant obesity and adult obesity are the same: insulin.

Babies born to mothers with gestational diabetes mellitus are at three times the risk of obesity and diabetes in later life. Surprisingly, a major risk factor for obesity in young adulthood is obesity in childhood. Obese children are at great risks of becoming obese adults! Even large-for-gestational-age babies whose mothers do not have gestational diabetes are also at risk. Sadly, what is happening is that we are now passing on our obesity to our children. Because the children absorb so much insulin starting in the womb, they develop more severe obesity sooner than ever before. And because obesity is time dependent and gets worse, fat babies become fat children. Fat children become fat adults. And fat adults have fat babies in turn, passing obesity on to the next generation.

LESSONS AND TAKEAWAYS

- Eat less, move more: a hoax!
- Obesity is not limited to adults.
- Childhood obesity has increased rapidly over the years.
- Childhood obesity results in adult obesity.

QUESTIONS

1. Insulin causes obesity; in adults, newborns, children and infants. How do you feel knowing that even the baby in the womb is prone to being obese?

    ____

    ____

    ____

    ____

2. How can this be combated?

3. Calories and weight gain/weight loss. Do you suppose there's any association between these two? Provide reasons for your choice.

4. Despite the continual failure of the low fat, low calorie diet, it is still being tried as a means of weight loss. What exactly is the deal?

ACTION STEPS

- Stop snacking.
- Reduce your consumption of sugars and starches.

CHECKLIST

- Instead of consuming high-sugar drinks, consume water.
- Instead of snacks, feed on fruits and vegetables.

PART 5: WHAT'S WRONG WITH OUR DIET?

CHAPTER 14: THE DEADLY EFFECTS OF FRUTOSE

Universally, it is accepted that sugar is fattening. Time and time again, we have been warned about the deadly dangers that lie in excessive sugar consumption. However, this message became lost in the wind as many people got caught up in the anti-fat campaign so much that people totally forgot about sugar, and buried all of their consciousness into avoiding fat. Year in, year out, different forms of sweets and candies were churned out in large quantities, all of them claiming to be fat free. And it didn't seem to bother anyone that they contained virtually a hundred percent sugar. Between 1977 and 2000, the rate of sugar consumption shot high, matching obesity rates. In a space of ten years, diabetes followed.

Glucose is a sugar that almost every cell in the human body. In the brain, it is the preferred energy source. Some cells can even only use glucose for energy. Glucose can be stored in the body in various forms such as glycogen in the liver. As a matter of fact, if glucose runs low in the system storage, the liver is capable of making new glucose via the process of glucone-ogenesis.

Fructose is another sugar mainly found in fruits. Fructose does not circulate in the blood, but is metabolized only in the liver. Most of the tissues cannot make direct use of fructose for energy. The consumption of fructose does not particularly affect the blood glucose level. In a research conducted by Dr. David Jenkins, foods were reclassified according to their blood glucose effect. This led to the development of the glycemic index. At the end of the study, it was discovered that fructose, unlike glucose, has an extremely low glycemic index.

Fructose is by far the most dangerous sugar there is. Strangely, fructose does not raise the blood sugar, but is strongly connected to obesity and diabetes, far more than glucose is. Like glucose, fructose is of no essential, nutritional value. As sweeteners, they function alike. However, with regards to the human health, fructose appears malicious. Initially, people preferred fructose sweeteners because of its low glycemic level. But with the introduction of high fructose corn syrup, things took a spiky route. By the year 2000, fructose had peaked at 9 per cent of total calories, and adolescents were already consuming 72.8 grams of fructose per day.

Because only the liver can metabolize fructose, an excessive consumption puts a lot of pressure on the liver owing to the inability of the other organs to help. Also, while the body system has several means by which it handles excess glucose consumption, there is none to handle same for fructose. Hence, the more you eat, the more metabolism your system undergoes. Bottom line is this: excess fructose is converted to fat in the liver, causing fatty liver. And fatty liver is extremely central to the development of insulin resistance in the liver.

LESSONS AND TAKEAWAYS

- Sugar is fattening.

- Sugar is toxic.
- Diabetes correlates with sugar, not calories.
- The big problem? Fructose!

QUESTIONS

1. What caused a decline in the popularity of sugar-sweetened soft drinks?

____

____

____

____

2. Despite the attendant risks that come with sugar consumption, many continue to indulge themselves. What could be the reason behind this?

____

____

____

____

3. The difference between sucrose and fructose is thin. Why is fructose a problem?

____

____

____

____

4. Why was it important to classify food according to their blood glucose effect?

____

____

____

____

5. How important is the glycemic index?

____

____

____

____

ACTION STEPS

- Remove all added sugars from your diet
- Do not replace them with artificial sweeteners

CHECKLIST

- Excessive fructose puts a whole lot of pressure on the liver
- Excess fructose becomes fat in the liver, causing fatty liver

CHAPTER 15: THE DIET SODA DELUSION

Sometime in 1879, Constantin Fahlberg discovered saccharin, the first artificial sweetener in the world. Initially, saccharin was synthesized as a drink additive, especially for diabetics. Soon enough however, its popularity spread and other low calorie compounds like Cyclamate and Aspartame were synthesized. Different calorie compounds have evolved over the years, but the most prominent of all currently is sucralose, which is most common in diet drinks, as well as in some yogurts, snack bars, cereals and a host of other foods that have been termed sugar-free.

The diet drink composition is made up of few calories, and no sugar. Hence, it makes every sense to replace a regular soft drink with a diet soda, as a means of reducing sugar intake and losing some weight. Owing to this, food manufacturers capitalized on the demand for sugar free food, releasing an estimated six thousand new artificially sweetened products, resulting in a twenty to twenty five per cent consumption of these foods by Americans, mostly in beverages.

However, as the years went by, there arose needs to investigate whether or not these artificial sweeteners were helpful. According to a research conducted by Dr. Sharon Fowler, diet beverages played no role in reducing obesity, but instead, increased the chances by a mind blowing forty-seven percent. Further research revealed that rather than fighting obesity, artificial sweeteners were fuelling it.

LESSONS AND TAKEAWAYS

- Artificial sweeteners are not any better than sugar itself.
- Diet drinks don't help curb or reduce obesity, or diabetes.

- Artificial sweetener use fuels, rather than fights, the obesity epidemic.
- Artificial sweeteners are bad!

QUESTIONS

1. Despite being really low in caloric levels, artificial sweeteners do not help reduce obesity. Why is this so?

 ____

 ____

 ____

 ____

2. In practical sense, have you ever come across anyone who drinks diet soda and lost a lot of weight as a result?

 ____

 ____

 ____

 ____

3. The health implications attached to the consumption of diet soda are weighty. Is it really worth it?

 ____

 ____

 ____

 ____

ACTION STEPS

- Focus on insulin, not calories.
- Do away with artificial sweeteners.

CHECKLIST

- Reducing dietary sugar is beneficial, but shouldn't be replaced with artificial sweeteners.

CHAPTER 16: CARBOHYDRATES AND PROTECTIVE FIBER

For many years, carbohydrates were considered a harmless class of food, low in fat and perhaps, man's liberation from the heart disease epidemic; until the Atkins' onslaught which named them dietary villains. As a result, many advocates abandoned carbohydrates, all of them- fruits and vegetables inclusive. However, not all carbohydrates are bad.

Obesity is driven majorly by insulin and insulin resistance. The greatest insulin levels are caused by white sugar and white flour. Yes, these are pretty fattening foods, but it doesn't imply that all carbohydrates are bad. There are good carbohydrates in the form of while fruits and vegetables, and they differ greatly from the bad carbohydrates which usually take the form of sugar and flour. Broccoli, for instance, regardless of how much of it you consume, will not make you fat. But even seemingly modest sugar quantities will result in weight gain. It is important therefore to know how to differentiate between both.

The major approach to this is the glycemic index and glycemic load, which help you know and understand the carbohydrate makeup of fruits and foods, and its effect on blood glucose. For instance, the carbohydrate levels of a watermelon is nothing compared to what is present in corn. Hence, being armed with this knowledge does help in determining healthy serving sizes. In the western part of the world, most refined foods have very high glycmic index and glycemic load scores, while most traditional foods have low glycemic stores.

LESSONS AND TAKEAWAYS

- There are good carbohydrates, and they differ greatly from bad carbs.
- Glycemic index and glycemic load.
- Refining increases the glycemic index of the carbohydrate.
- Refining encourages overconsumption.

QUESTIONS

1. 'Weight gain is not driven by blood glucose, but by insulin and cortisol.' What is your understanding of this statement?

   ____

   ____

   ____

   ____

2. Why has the focus been on lowering glucose levels, instead of insulin levels?

   ____

   ____

   ____

   ____

3. Is glucose the only stimulant to insulin secretion?

   ____

   ____

   ____

   ____

ACTION STEPS

- Adopt the use of vinegar in your diets.

CHECKLIST

- Vinegar may help reduce insulin resistance.
- Do not expect rapid weight loss with the use of vinegar.

CHAPTER 17: PROTEIN

As the tides turned against carbohydrates, the medical community began advocating all sorts, beginning with castigating carbohydrate reduced diets, as being unbalanced, which appeared to make good sense. Truthfully, there are only three macronutrients: protein, fat and carbohydrate. And by restricting any of these severely, it sure sounded like risking an unbalanced diet. However, while the concern lay about how balanced or unbalanced these diets were, very little attention was paid to whether or not the diets were healthy or unhealthy.

For instance, if we insist that diets low in carbs are unbalanced; do we imply that the nutrients contained in carbohydrates are essential for human health? The answer is a resounding No. carbohydrates are just long chains of sugars. Period! Hence, it is only wise that low carbohydrate diets that lay emphasis on letting go of refined grains and sugars should be encouraged, as they are healthier. These diets may not be balanced, but they're healthy.

Diets rich in protein are recommended for people with normal kidney function. Hitherto, we had been made to believe that high protein diets may not particularly work for weight loss. However, this notion is incorrect. Like carbohydrates, dietary proteins could also cause a surge in insulin levels.

LESSONS AND TAKEAWAYS

- A healthy, unbalanced diet is ten times better than an unhealthy, balanced diet.
- Much of the initial weight loss experienced by dieters is water.

- High protein diets did not work for weight loss.
- Dietary proteins can cause a surge similar to that of refined carbohydrates.

QUESTIONS

1. With protein, is there any correlation between blood glucose and insulin levels?

   ____

   ____

   ____

   ____

2. What was the mistake made by glycemic index diets?

   ____

   ____

   ____

   ____

3. Why is oral glucose better than intravenous, at stimulating insulin?

   ____

   ____

   ____

   ____

ACTION STEPS

- If you are not hungry, do not eat.

CHECKLIST

- Animal protein varies highly

CHAPTER 18: FAT PHOBIA

Several years ago, a huge discovery was made by Dr. Ancel keys. The renowned physician discovered that Americans, regardless of how well-nourished they were, continually suffered from rising rates of heart attack and stroke. In Europe however, these rates were low, despite being ravaged by war. And taking a cue from the Mediterranean diet, and comparing it alongside the regular American diet, he came up with a set of recommendations which had as its central message that all fat is bad, the worst of all being saturated fats. This, which is in error by the way, resulted in the acceptance of the diet heart hypothesis. And as the years rolled by, animal fat consumption began a relentless decline, with carbohydrates climbing, all of which were detrimental to the human health.

LESSONS AND TAKEAWAYS

- Reduce your consumption of saturated fat
- Consume vegetable oils, instead of solid fats
- Saturated fats are dangerous.

QUESTIONS

1. What causes heart disease?

____

____

____

____

2. What was the previous link between cholesterol and heart disease?

____

____

____

____

3. In the true sense of things, what is cholesterol? What does cholesterol do for your body system?

____

____

____

____

ACTION STEPS

- Consume a good amount of Omega 6's
- Eat flax seeds, walnuts and oily fish, as they are all good sources of Omega 3.
- There must be a balance in the consumption of these oils, as an imbalance could worsen cardiovascular diseases.

CHECKLIST

- Eating fat does not make you fat, but may protect you against it.

PART 6: THE SOLUTION

CHAPTER 19: WHAT TO EAT

Over the years, with lots of dietary studies, two remarkable discoveries have been made. The first is that all diets work. And the second, being that all diets fail. In basic terms, weight loss follows the pattern peculiar to dieters. Regardless of what pattern one decides to follow, weight loss is achieved in the short term. They all appear to work, until you have to begin a relentless, unending weight regain, despite continued dietary compliance.

And this is why diets fail. Permanent weight loss involves two steps. The hypothalamic region of the brain determines the body set weight. Here, insulin acts to set the body weight higher. In the short term, we can apply different diets to bring our body weight down. But once it falls below the set weight, the body activates mechanisms to regain the weight, this, is the long term problem.

Obesity is a hormonal disorder, a fat regulation problem. Hence, the only way to permanently keep the weight away is to reduce insulin levels, as insulin is the major hormone that drives weight gain. Reduce your consumption of added sugars like fructose and sucrose. Let go of the sugar bowl. Consume dark chocolates, and do away with snacks. Make breakfast optional, it's not so necessary anyway. Drink plain water, coffee and tea. Reduce your consumption of refined grains. Moderate your protein consumption, and lastly, increase your consumption of natural fat and protective factors.

LESSONS AND TAKEAWAYS

- Depending on how we look at things, all diets work, and all diets fail.\
- In the short term, all diets appear to produce some result.
- Weight loss, on a permanent level, is a two-step process.
- Your body has a set weight.

QUESTIONS

1. Why do all diets fail?

   ____

   ____

   ____

   ____

2. Is there a single cause of obesity?

   ____

   ____

   ____

   ____

3. If your response to (2) above was in the affirmative, state what the cause is and how it works.

   ____

   ____

   ____

   ____

4. If you responded to (2) above in the negative, provide reasons for your choice.

   ____

   ____

____

____

5. Obesity is a multi-factorial disease. What is your opinion on this?

____

____

____

____

ACTION STEPS

- Consume dark chocolates
- Do away with snacks.
- Drink plain water, coffee and tea.

CHECKLIST

- The only way to permanently keep the weight away is to reduce insulin levels

CHAPTER 20: WHEN TO EAT

The body reacts to weight loss by trying to return to its original body size. And even though we often hope that our original body set weight will decrease over a period of time, it almost never happens. Our insulin levels always stay high.

As earlier noted, weight loss is a two-step process. The first is that we must mind what we eat, which is usually what changes whenever a decision is made to embark on a diet. However, there is another factor which is the problem of meal-timing. Insulin resistance keeps our insulin levels high, and so, because of our already set body levels, our weight loss levels are often eroded. We begin to feel hungrier, body metabolism increases, and gradually, our weight returns to its original size, despite our consistent dieting. Hence, changing what we eat is not always enough. We must do all we can to break the insulin resistance cycle which can only be done by increasing insulin levels, which actually goes on to create more resistance. However, in order to break it, we must have recurrent periods of very low insulin levels. And in order to induce our bodies into a state of low insulin levels, we must fast. The key word here is fasting.

We fast to break insulin resistance, and consequently, to lose weight. This kind of fast involves intermittent fast of twenty to thirty six hours. It is an ancient remedy to help break insulin resistance. Fasting does not necessarily mean starvation. Unlike starvation, fasting is voluntary, and is embarked upon for health, spiritual or other reasons. It is a part of life, and the truth is that on many occasions, people break their fast with breakfast. When you fast, you put the body in a state where it begins to make use of glucose and fat. When glucose is no longer available, your body adjusts by using fat, with no health detriment. All the hormones adjust to fasting, and contrary to what people think about fasting, it is important for you to know that of all of the myths they hold about fasting were true, none of us would be alive today. Fasting is important, and is the only true means by which you can control when you eat, so as to help you lose weight, permanently.

LESSONS AND TAKEAWAYS

- In the long run, dieting is a futile exercise. The weight always returns.
- There is a problem of meal timing which must be addressed.
- The insulin-resistance cycle must be broken in order to succeed.
- Fasting: the long lasting solution!

QUESTIONS

1. What do you know fasting to mean?

____

____

____

____

2. Is fasting the same thing as starvation?

____

____

____

____

3. Fasting is equivalent to cleansing the human body. How does this work?

____

____

____

____

ACTION STEPS

- Do not be afraid. You can fast. And nothing will happen to you, negatively.
- Actually, you should fast. Your body needs it, and so do you!
- Begin by simply skipping a few meals. Skip a meal today, will you?

CHECK LIST

- In many cases, fasting is accompanied by a rapid weight loss.
- Fasting can be combined with any diet; any at all.

CPSIA information can be obtained
at www.ICGtesting.com
Printed in the USA
BVHW050032250121
598589BV00004B/344

9 781950 284290